RED SQUIRRI

RED SQUIRRELS ON THE
ISLE OF WIGHT

RED SQUIRRELS

THE STORY OF
RED SQUIRRELS
ON THE ISLE OF WIGHT

Helen Butler
and
John Norledge

Published by Coach House Publications Ltd.
The Coach House, School Green Road,
Freshwater, Isle of Wight.

Printed by West Island Printers Ltd.
Afton Road, Freshwater, Isle of Wight, PO40 9TT

CONTENTS

CONSERVATION

Endangered species
The 'Berne' convention
EC Habitat Directive
Earth Summit at Rio
Work being done
Reintroductions and captive breeding
National strategy for saving the Red Squirrel
Importance of I.o.W. in national context
Conservation of Red Squirrels on the Isle of Wight
What you can do to help
The Future

APPENDIX 1.

Where to find squirrels on the Isle of Wight
Tourist attractions visited by squirrels

APPENDIX 2.

Organisations supporting Red Squirrels

APPENDIX 3.

Reporting Red Squirrel sightings
Reporting dead squirrels
What to do if you find an injured squirrel

APPENDIX 4.

Red Squirrel sighting sheets

LIST OF PHOTOGRAPHS, MAPS, DIAGRAMS and TABLES

PHOTOGRAPHS

MAPS

DIAGRAMS

TABLES

ACKNOWLEDGEMENTS

Thanks to John Norledge for writing the general squirrel details - leaving me time to concentrate on the information specific to the Isle of Wight - and his encouragement and help to meet a tight deadline.

My thanks to S.C.O.P.E. members and everyone else who has contributed squirrel sightings and general information, particulary people who allowed me access to their private woods. Special thanks to those who have supplied coffee and biscuits while I have sat looking out of their windows, with a camera perched on my lap, in the hope of photographing a squirrel. Without you I would not have the majority of the pictures in this book.

As you read through the I.o.W. information and anecdotes you will notice that few individuals names or exact private locations which squirrels visit are mentioned. This is to preserve the privacy of those people who are lucky enough to have resident squirrels.

I would also like to express my gratitude to Dr. Jessica Holm, Dr. John Gurnell, Dr. Robert Kenward, Monica Shorten, David Stapleford and other researchers in this field whose work has increased our knowledge and understanding of squirrel ecology.

Last, but by no means least, very many thanks to Dr. Colin Pope, the staff of the Countryside Management Service at Parkhurst and to Val Gwynn for their continuing support and guidance.

PREFACE

I came into surveying Red Squirrels on the Isle of Wight by accident. After being made redundant from an office job, I decided to try something different. Having always preferred the outdoor life, conservation seemed a good idea and I was recruited to the BTCV (British Trust for Conservation Volunteers).

They say never volunteer for anything - well I volunteered to pick up used hazelnuts for the BTCV'S hazelnut survey in the autumn of 1991 and have been scrabbling in the leaf litter ever since. Frank Heap, then field officer for the BTCV, really started the ball rolling with an article in the County Press asking for people to 'phone in with squirrel sightings. The unprecented response from all parts of the Island kept me busy seven days a week for months. Sightings were reported from places I didn't even know existed and I often found myself in the 'back of beyond'.

I have now visited virtually all of the woodland on the Island and have amassed an ever growing mountain of data about our 'Island Reds'. I have also formed a small group, S.C.O.P.E. (Species Conservation Organisation Protecting the Environment), which helps me collect Red Squirrel information on an Islandwide basis and carries out practical conservation work to improve the habitat for wildlife.

Inspiration to put pen to paper came from a realisation that the general public needed to be made more aware of the plight of the Red Squirrel, its rapid and seemingly irreversible national decline in the face of competition from the introduced Grey Squirrel and the associated conservation issues suurounding its continued survival on the mainland. I also felt that wider publicity should be given to the special position of the Red Squirrel on the Isle of Wight to highlight the need to sustain and improve the habitat here to secure a long term future.

This book is the result. I have tried to convey my enthusiasm and concern for this popular and fascinating species in a scientifically accurate but readable way and I hope you will agree that we should do all we can to ensure that the Red Squirrel remains an everyday part of the Island scene for the forseeable future.

Helen Butler

INTRODUCTION

There can be few Isle of Wight residents who have not had the pleasure of seeing a Red Squirrel.

Sometimes it is a nerve-jangling experience; slamming on the brakes to avoid a death-defying youngster hesitating in the middle of the road before scampering on to the church wall at Brook. On other occasions it is a more relaxed meeting around the picnic tables at Parkhurst Forest where the promise of a free meal has a magnetic attraction. Perhaps the silence of a winter walk in the woods at Newtown is broken by the scalding calls of an indignant resident caught in the act of raiding its food store or maybe you are one of the lucky few who have Red Squirrels regularly visiting their gardens and can recognise them as individuals in their own right each with its own special character and characteristics.

Such encounters with this delightful creature, although frequent here on the Island, are sadly a thing of the past for much of England where the Grey Squirrel continues its apparently unstoppable advance, displacing the Red Squirrel as it goes.

The narrow strip of water which separates the Island from the mainland has so far proved to be an impenetrable barrier for the grey invader from North America so the Red Squirrel survives here, much as it had done for thousands of years on the mainland, as the only squirrel native to the British Isles. So the Island's population which exists without threat or competition from the Grey is both special in a local sense and important in national terms.

SQUIRREL FACT
The Latin name for the Red Squirrel is Sciurus vulgaris. Sciurus originates from the Greek word 'skioros' which means 'shade-tail'.

This book tells the story of the Red Squirrel on the Isle of Wight looking at its distribution, status and all aspects of its lifestyle. The situation of the Reds on the mainland and the impact of the introduction of the Grey Squirrel is covered, particular attention being paid to conservation matters and the question of the future survival of the Red Squirrel in Britain as a whole.

World Range

The Red Squirrel occupies a broad band of territory running from the seaboard of Western Europe and Scandinavia through what was formerly the U.S.S.R. and Mongolia to North East China including Sakhalin Island and Hokkaido the most northerly of the Japanese islands.

Throughout this vast geographical range the Red Squirrel reigns supreme and with the exception of Japan and Iran it is the only squirrel species to be found. This situation contrasts dramatically with North America where there are 15 species of Sciurus squirrels alone and in tropical regions of the world the diversity is even more marked.

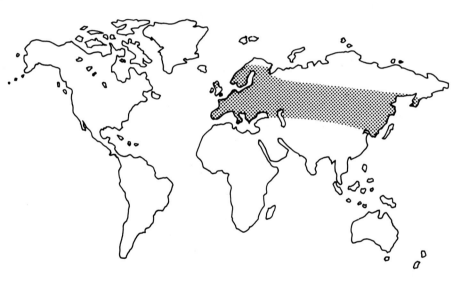

Map 1 - World Distribution

The reason for this situation is believed to relate to the stability of the environment. Where conditions remain unchanged over long periods of time, millions of years in the case of the rain forests, a vast array of interdepedant plant and animal species has the opportunity to evolve. However, where the goal posts are regularly moved, only relatively few species can gain a foothold. So the repeated glaciations of the northerly latitudes, which periodically replaced the forests with arctic tundra, have resulted in a much reduced variety of seed bearing trees which in turn support only a small number of tree seed eaters.

Within the global territory occupied by the Red Squirrel there are many subspecies. There may in fact be a unique race of British Squirrels which has evolved slight but distinct differences from their continental cousins but this 'distinctiveness' has probably been blurred by introductions of European stock in the past when British squirrel numbers were at a low ebb.

Arrival in Britain

It is thought that the Red Squirrel arrived, or more accurately speaking, recolonised the British Isles after the end of the last 'Ice Age'. As the climate warmed and the glaciers melted and retreated, pine forest, a prime source of food for Red Squirrels, began to spread gradually northwards across what had been the frozen wastes of southern Britain. All this was happening at a time when the sea level was much lower than today and both Britain and Ireland were connected by land to the European continent. The squirrels were able to cross the land bridge and move northwards and westwards fanning out across the country, exploiting the food source provided by the pines. In this way they reached the Isle of Wight, which was then connected to the mainland.

The effects of rising sea level and the headward erosion of the southern tributaries of the Solent river eventually severed the narrow strip of land which linked what is now Old Harry Rocks near Studland in Dorset with the Needles at Alum Bay. The sea broke through about 5,000 ago. The Isle of Wight was formed and its population of squirrels effectively isolated.

ECOLOGY

This section looks at how Red Squirrels live generally but I have emphasised any particular instances where the the behaviour of Island squirrels appears to be different to that observed on the mainland.

Feeding

The Red Squirrel's main food is the seeds of trees - pine cones, hazel nuts, beech mast, oak acorns, etc. It is believed that the Red Squirrel evolved in conifer forest as this is where they reach their maximum numbers but it has adapted to live in broadleaved woods.

In mixed conifer forests the differing pace of development of the cones on different species of trees generally means that there is a good food supply all year round. No natural mixed conifer woods exist on the Island but plantations at Parkhurst, Bouldnor and Firestone Copse can provide a good food source with the seeds of the Corsican Pine being a particular favourite. The drawback of plantations is their limited variety of tree species with the prospect of food shortages if the seed crop is poor and, of course, these man-created habitats are subject to thinning and felling.

Deciduous woods offer a wider variety with the seeds of hazel, beech, oak, sweet chestnut, ash, field maple, and hornbeam all being eaten. Hazel is the most significant species. Breeding success is related to the quality of the hazel crop each year and numbers will fall if there are few nuts about. Squirrels try to prolong this strictly seasonal harvest by hoarding food, especially hazelnuts, which are buried in small caches all over the woodland floor. These scatter-hidden stores can be located by smell and are eaten throughout the winter and into the spring if stocks last.

SQUIRREL FACT
Squirrels can tell by the weight of a hazel nut whether or not it contains a juicy kernel and so do not waste valuable time and energy opening dud nuts.

On the Island squirrels also eat the acorns of the holm oak - a mediterranean tree planted here in Victorian times and the seeds of the monterey cypress - often referred to as the Macrocarpa - another introduced species, this time from the North American continent but grown widely across the Island as an ornamental tree.

SQUIRREL FACT
Red Squirrels cannot live on acorns alone - it is believed the tannins they contain cause digestive problems - they have to be eaten as part of a varied diet.

At other times of the year squirrels eat a wide variety of food eg. oak flowers, buds, catkins, shoots, roots and ripening wheat or barley. Bark-sap is obtained by stripping the bark from the branches or trunk and this used to be a problem on the mainland in commercial plantations where the squirrel was regarded as a pest. This habit does not seem to occur very often on the Island and the last time I saw an example was in Batts Copse near Shanklin in 1993 which was probably carried out at a time of poor food supply.

SQUIRREL FACT
Squirrels eat fungi . Some typical toadstool varieties are consumed but a species called Vuilleminia, found under the bark of dead or dying oak branches, is an important addition to the diet when other food is scarce.

The autumnal crop of berries and fruits - crab apples, hawthorn, blackthorn, etc. is vital but squirrels are opportunistic feeders and will also eat bulbs, insects and birds eggs. One brave individual in Porchfield was seen raiding a Magpie's nest! Instances of taking fledglings and consuming carrion have also been observed.

SQUIRREL FACT
A Red Squirrel should gain at least 10% of its bodyweight in fat, if it is to survive the winter.

Red Squirrels need to eat nutritious food and if only poor quality sustenance is available a squirrel may spend all day eating and still lose weight - more energy being lost through searching activity, than being gained from the actual food eaten.

SQUIRREL FACT
Like humans some squirrels are either right or left handed when stripping pine cones. Some clip off the scales with their teeth while others tear them off.

TABLE 1. Seasonal foods

Spring
Pine and various other conifer seeds.
Bark.
Buds, shoots and leaves of trees and shrubs, especially oak, birch and hazel.
Hazel and birch catkins.
Pollen.
Insects.
Blackthorn, wild garlic and bluebell flowers.
Stored hazel nuts.
Ripening ears of grain.

Summer
Pine and various other conifer seeds.
Bark.
Ash and field maple keys.
Fruits including crab apples, blackberries and rose hips.
Leaves and shoots of trees and shrubs.
Insects.

Autumn
Pine and various other conifer seeds.
Tree seeds including hazel nuts, sweet chestnuts, acorns, field maple keys and alder seeds.
Fruits including rose hips, blackberries and berries of hawthorn, guelder rose and wayfaring tree.
Leaves of trees and shrubs and fungi.

Winter
Pine and various other conifer seeds.
Bark.
Buds of trees and shrubs including hazel, birch, oak and field maple.
Leaves of trees and shrubs.
Fungi.
Stored hazel nuts.
Acorns.
Bulbs.
Carrion.
Insects.

A bank vole takes a neat slice from the top of the nut.

Dormice make a neat round hole. Note the patterned toothmarks around the edge.

A red squirrel notches the top of the nut, inserts an incisor and splits the nut in half.

A pine cone stripped by a red squirrel.

Woodmice gnaw a ragged hole in the nut and leave untidy toothmarks and scratches.

DIAGRAM 1.
Squirrel feeding signs - stripped cones and opened hazel nuts

Feeding activity reaches its peak once a day in winter and twice a day in summer and there is seasonal variation in the amount of time spent feeding of the ground and the amount of time spent searching the tree canopy for food.

Photo 1. Squirrel feeding (on natural food)

Table 2. Seasonal variation in foraging location

SQUIRREL FACT
Red Squirrels need to eat daily and if food intake is low because of poor weather or food shortage then they can quickly succomb to disease or starvation.

Squirrels are intelligent and quickly investigate and learn to accept new foods and take readily to 'artificial' feeding. People who are lucky enough to have squirrels visiting their gardens will tell you that squirrels are up at the crack of dawn to feed regardless of the season. Only the weather may make a difference. On sombre overcast mornings squirrels may have a lie in or they may have an early night if the skies are dark and threatening.

SQUIRREL FACT
Average squirrel time for splitting and eating a ripe hazelnut is 22 seconds.

Photo 2. - Squirrel feeding in garden

It is thought that squirrels obtain most of their needs for moisture from the food they eat or by drinking dew from leaves but my observations suggest that they will regularly take a drink if a convenient supply is avaliable. They are often seen drinking in gardens as the photograph on the following page shows and the fact that few squirrel have been seen drinking in woods probably just reflects the fact that there are few woodland ponds about.

Shelter

Red Squirrels do not hibernate and therefore need a home which keeps them warm and dry in the harsh and often freezing conditions of the winter months. If a squirrel gets cold and wet it can soon die of exposure. During the summer months a place to sleep and to raise a family is required. These needs are provided by building dreys.

SQUIRREL FACT
A squirrel will usually have constructed several dreys
in its home range. Switching dreys helps to prevent a build
up of lice and fleas.

Dreys are dome shaped structures usually made from interwoven branches and leaves. Summer dreys may only be temporary constructions and are not as robust as those built to give protection during the winter. These are well constructed and can last for several seasons.

Photo 3. - Squirrel drinking

Sometimes, however, squirrels will use a variety of other materials if they are to hand. One drey found at Nokes Common was lined with the stuffing from a discarded mattress. This drey could be examined closely because it was one of several blown from the trees during a gale. Inexperienced squirrels sometimes build their dreys in the tops of trees or in the outer branches but those which are best suited to survive the ravages of high winds and storms are those placed either close to the trunk or in a fork of the tree.

Another unusual 'drey incident' I came across involved the theft of insulation from a caravan roof. This particular squirrel's drey presumably needed a warm lining and, using a clematis to reach the roof, the squirrel proceded to take the insulation away! It had the right idea anyway! The caravan owner solved the problem by cutting down the clematis.

SQUIRREL FACT
Dreys are built in both deciduous trees and conifers.

When available, squirrels will live in holes in trees. In woods with many old trees these 'dens' may be quite common but in conifer plantations sizeable trees with holes are a distinct rarity.

Photo 4. Drey in the fork of a tree

Photo 5 . Drey with mattress stuffing and honeysuckle bark

Photo 6. Squirrel using a 'den'

Every year we hear of birds building in odd places but the Island squirrels would appear to be strictly creatures of habit. I have not come across any unusual squirrel abodes nor have I had any confirmed reports of squirrels living in lofts or roof spaces in houses.

Pelage

Although we think of a Red Squirrels fur as being a gingery red colour there is a surprising degree of variation both at different times of the year and between different individuals.

The summer coat of the average squirrel is a rich chestnut. There may be grey fur around the flanks and head and the hairs on the ear-tufts and tail are bleached to a creamy-white. In winter the fur is dark brown. Tail colour is also dark brown but this gradulally begins to bleach and reverts to a cream colour by March although not all reds have bleached tails.

My experience of Island squirrels is that they are a very varied bunch indeed and that it is impossible to identify a Mr or Mrs Average. Variation in colour, in addition to seasonal differences, is quite common and ranges from a pale ginger to darker red and brown shades. Squirrels with light tails can be seen all the year round and these individuals tend to have gingery coats.

Grey colouring can also be found and these squirrels can often be mistaken for grey squirrels especially when the ear-tufts have been moulted.

All black (melanistic) squirrels do occur rarely. One was seen recently in the Rowridge area in 1993 but has not so far been spotted in 1994. Pale, white and albino squirrels are supposed to occur more frequently than the all black form but, here on the Island, I have not yet seen or come across a recent report of a white squirrel. It is thought that these individuals do not live as long as those with 'normal' fur colours because they are not so well camouflaged and therefore easier for predators to find.

In 1993 at Brook several squirrels could be found with white flecking in their fur. It will be interesting to see whether this unusual mutation continues down the generations.

Photo 7 - Summer coat minus eartufts

Photo 8 - Winter coat with eartufts

Photo 9 - Red Squirrel with a grey coat

The experts are very interested in the colour variations found in British Red Squirrels because they could help to throw light on the origins of these animals. Are they a separate race or are they the same as the squirrels across the Channel in Europe? Light-tailed squirrels are not often seen in the mainland populations but here, on the Island, this characteristic is common. Does this mean Island squirrels are more closely related to an indigenous ancestor? Perhaps only the scientific analysis of the squirrel's D.N.A. 'fingerprint' will solve this mystery once and for all.

SQUIRREL FACT
Squirrels have 20 pairs of chromosomes
- humans have 23 pairs.

Photo 10 - Grey Squirrel

Photos 11a & 11b: comparison different colour forms - 'blood brothers or distant cousins?'

Photo 12 - Mating chase or pecking order in action

Breeding

There are roughly equal numbers of males and females but squirrels are promiscuous and do not form stable relationships. Males take no part at all in raising the offspring a task which falls exclusively to the female.

Sexual maturity is reached at approximately 11 months of age. Males are ready to mate at any time of year although some become sexually inactive between September and November. Females can produce two litters a year with an average of three youngsters in each litter. Gestation takes approximately 38 days.

SQUIRREL FACT
Breeding is dependent on the availability of a good food supply and will not take place if squirrels are hungry or in poor physical condition.

Romance in the squirrel world is a frenetic affair. The males are first attracted by the females scent. The keenest suitor follows the female closely signalling his excitement with tail swishing and loud chattering calls. A mating chase then takes place through the trees and around the tree trunks with other males joining in. The chase is repeated until the female allows one of the males to mate with her.

SQUIRREL FACT
The mating chase may last for two days and is something of an endurance test for the males. The survival of the fittest!

Litters can be produced at any time of the year but the majority of young are born between March and April and June and July. On the Island litters have been recorded as early as January and as late as September.

Squirrel mothers may decide to move home before their offspring are old enough to 'hop'. Two methods of transportation have been observed on the Island in the past three years. Firstly, the 'piggy back' and secondly one baby was seen clinging around its mother's neck.

TABLE 3 - Development of the young squirrels

1. Red Squirrels are born blind, toothless, pink and without hair.

2. Hair has usually appeared by day eight and by about two weeks the body will be lightly covered with hair.

3. The incisors, the first teeth to appear, do so after three weeks.

4. At four weeks the eyes and ears open and the teeth will have appeared.

5. By seven weeks the youngsters begin to venture out of the nest for the first time and although they are still suckling they will try solid food.

6. At ten weeks suckling is almost finished. The mother forages further afield and may not return to the nest every night. By this time all the milk teeth have come through.

7. Between ten and fourteen weeks the juveniles begin to move out to a new nest and start to live independently.

8. The young moult and gain their first adult coat around the four month mark.

9. Between four and eight months the milk teeth are lost and replaced by the adult set.

SQUIRREL FACT
The incisors are not lost but continue to grow throughout
the life of the squirrel.

Photo 13 - Young squirrel - notice in particular the large feet.

Pecking order

Although our Reds are nowhere near as aggressive as their grey cousins they do squabble amongst themselves and there is a definite pecking order. Top spot might go to an adult male in breeding condition or a large female. Age, size and gender are all important factors in deciding who feeds on the best nuts. Smaller males or females and sub-adults jostle for position and sort out the next tier in the hierarchy while the juveniles are definitely at the end of the food queue. If you have ever watched a number of squirrels arrive together at a feeding table this behaviour is very apparant and is accompanied by a great deal of tail swishing and chuk-ckukking sounds. Occasionally squirrels fight in earnest and lose a toe or a chunk of fur, but tail swishing, swearing and chasing are the usual methods of sorting out dominance.

Dispersal

As they become more independent the young squirrels need to compete with other squirrels in the locality to establish their own livng space. If squirrel density is low there may be unoccupied ranges nearby although these are generally the poorer areas for food often on the periphery of the wood. When territories are in short supply the young squirrels, being at the bottom of the pecking order, lose out in the dominance stakes and have to look elsewhere for living quarters. Dispersal will then take place and as the majority of woods on the Island are small squirrels may be forced to cross open country, sometimes for considerable distances, to find a suitable home.

It is this dispersal behaviour that often leads to sightings of squirrels in unusual places or reports of squirrel taking up temporary residence in unsuitable sites.

Unusual sightings

Yarmouth school had a visit from a squirrel in September 1992. It was seen in the holm oak trees of the school grounds and later in a garden in Mill Road where it jumped up at the french windows. This squirrel may have originated from Bouldnor, Mill Copse or Thorley Copse and as an outside possibility it could have crossed the Yar bridge from Saltern Wood.

SQUIRREL FACT
In the late 80's a Red Squirrel appeared in Hansford's, the furniture shop, in Cross Street in Ryde, after climbing a sheer wall to reach the fourth floor. There were no cones left on this pine!

During the autumn of 1992 I found nuts split by squirrels in a series of small isolated woods and copses in the south of the Island. The trail led from Gotten via Wydcome to Brierly. There is not sufficient food in this area for a squirrel to set up home and the most likely explanation is that this was the route taken by a dispersing juvenile. Chances of long-term survival in this district would be poor.

In May 1992 a squirrel was seen travelling from the Goldenhill Fort area of Freshwater to Totland where it settled in a garden and built a drey, from grass clippings, in a Monterey Cypress. It stayed for a month before disappearing.

Also in the West Wight a squirrel was seen where Wilmingham Lane joins the Newport Road on the the outskirts of Freshwater. This individual probably originated from Wilmingham plantation but its destination is anyone's guess as there is no suitable habitat in that locality.

Squirrels have also been seen occasionally in the centre of Newport and in 1962 the County Press reported that shoppers in Ryde were surprised when a Red Squirrel dashed the full length of Union Street and disappeared along the sea front in the direction of Eastern Gardens.

In the early nineties a bold squirrel mysteriously appeared on board a yacht in the Medina river. The 'Nutkin Nations' first racing squirrel or a late Cowes entrant?

Photo 14. Conifer plantation

Mortality

By far the largest number of deaths occur in the juvenile population before the first year is reached. These squirrels are inexperienced and in years of poor food supply may simply die of starvation. At this stage they are easy prey for predators and because they often disperse to find a home range they run the gauntlet of road traffic with the inevitable result.

SQUIRREL FACT
Five out of six youngsters do not live to see their
first birthday.

Once the first year of life has been safely negotiated a five or six year life-span can be expected. The main cause of adult deaths is still however starvation. The Red Squirrel has no regular predators but individuals are sometimes caught by foxes and stoats. Analysis of barn owl pellets reveals that they also capture squirrels occasionally. This behaviour must be a very rarely observed event indeed but I do have one eye-witness report.

In some areas of the mainland goshawks prey on squirrels but this is a rare bird on the Island and numbers of squirrels taken must be minimal. Dogs infrequently snatch a unwary squirrel victim but the domestic cat is responsible for the majority of recorded deaths caused by predation. Not all cats are squirrel hunters and most co-exist quite amicably but once a rogue feline gets a taste for squirrel blood it can decimate a local population. I have two records of cats killing seven squirrels in a matter of months, one from the northeast of the Island and one from the northwest.

Another major cause of Island deaths is the car. Particularly vulnerable are the populations where woodland borders a busy main road or where the road interrupts a squirrel 'corridor'. Deaths peak during the mating season, between April and July, when the males are searching for females and later when the juveniles are dispersing to find home ranges of their own. Food shortages may also lead to squirrels foraging further afield and crossing roads in the process. Such carnage can severely deplete and in some cases eliminate altogether localised populations.

SQUIRREL FACT
In 1993 seven squirrel road deaths occurred at
Lushington Hill.

Squirrel numbers are periodically reduced by disease. Coccidosis is a type of enteritus causing wasting, severe diaorrhea and death. Parapoxvirus affects the eyelids which become puffy and swollen and in this way resembles myxomatosis. This debilitating disease is also fatal but I have only had one report of it occuring here on the Island..

Occasionally squirrels manage to get themselves killed in the most unusual ways. Some are drowned, most frequenty in farm troughs. Once the squirrels have fallen in they cannot get a grip on the smooth, steep sides, but one was reported to have lost its life in the millrace at Shalfleet. Other squirrels are poisoned or become trapped - one died in this way in a corn hopper at Shorwell - and Jessica Holm, in her book 'Squirrels', recalls two bizarre incidents; one squirrel was run over by a steam train and another was ploughed to death. Thank goodness Red Squirrels are no longer persecuted as pests because of their habit of bark stripping.

SQUIRREL FACT

Culling of Red Squirrels was carried out
in the New Forest until 1927 and between 1903 and
1933 the Highland Squirrel Club killed 82,000 squirrels.

TABLE 4. Bar Chart showing analysis of Island deaths

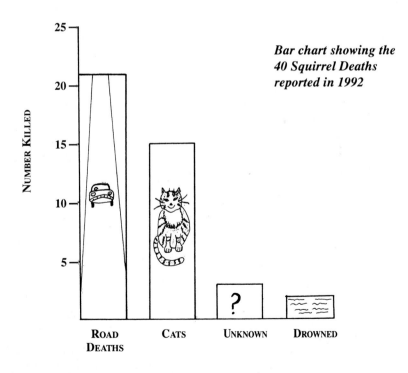

Bar chart showing the 40 Squirrel Deaths reported in 1992

Photo 15 - Fox

Photo 16 - Barn Owl

Photo 17 -
Squirrel road death

Photo 18 - Squirrel resting in tree

Also gone are the days when squirrels were killed for sport. The Observer's Book of Wild Animals (1954) recalls the time when the situation and our cultural appreciation of the Red Squirrel was very different.

' In the neighbourhood of large towns the 'sporting instinct' of ignorant people has led them to kill and mutilate squirrels with sticks and stones. Not many years ago the numerous squirrels that added to the attractions of Richmond Park were shot by the keepers to prevent them being killed in this way. Ordinary intelligences thought it would have been better to have disciplined the offenders'

Can we prevent any Squirrel deaths?

The answer is yes! Do not encourage squirrels to visit your garden if they have to cross a busy road to get there or if you have a cat which kills squirrels. There may also be a case for having 'squirrel crossing' signs on known danger spots, in much the same way that toad/duck crossing points are indicated. Supplementary feeding may be vital for squirrel survival in times of food shortages.

DIAGRAM 2. - Squirrel Road Crossing Sign

Dead squirrels can be sent away for a post mortem. This may reveal the cause of death for example by poisoning or be the first indication of the spread of disease.

SQUIRREL FACT
Please report the finding of any dead squirrel to:
Wight Wildlife   (See Appendix 3 for the address.)

Home ranges and habitat requirements

Red squirrels do not have strictly defined territorial boundaries but live in home ranges which are partly shared with the neighbouring squirrels. The size of the range varies with the type of habitat and the food supply available, ie the poorer the food supply the larger the range. As a rough guide, one hectare (two and a half acres) of good habitat will support one squirrel. Squirrels will reach good numbers in a variety of wooded habitats.

SQUIRREL FACT
Although solitary for the most part in cold or wet conditions squirrels will share their dreys and huddle up together for warmth.

Conifer Woods
Pine forests are the Red Squirrels ancestral home and although this type of wood does not exist on the Island there are some reasonably large tracts of conifer plantation which, with their year-round supply of cones, provide some of the best squirrel habitat to be found locally.

Broadleaved Woods

Old broadleaved woodland, where natural regeneration or coppicing allows light to reach the understorey shrubs, is also good squirrel habitat and the mixture of tree species present is an advantage because if one seed crop fails another food source will be available.

> **SQUIRREL FACT**
> Red Squirrels prefer a closed canopy which provides cover and facilitates travel amongst the branches without touching the ground.

Coppice

Squirrels actively avoid new coppice and the best rotation is believed to be a 15-20 year cycle. This is longer than most commercial coppicing currently carried out which is cropped every 7-10 years. A coppiced stool on the Island, where there are no deer to nibble away at the young shoots, will start to produce a significant number of nuts 5 years after coppicing.

Photo 19 - New coppice

> **SQUIRREL FACT**
> Coppicing - the system of regularly cutting trees just above ground level to produce a crop of thin straight poles - was developed in neolithic times.

Photo 20 - Grown coppice

Photo 21 - Jeff filming squirrels

General

Wide rides and the woodland edge are also important features; not only does the amount of light received by these areas stimulate excellent production of hazelnuts, but they usually contain a whole range of other food sources for squirrel s eg. blackberries.

The final element in a habitat fit for a squirrel is a series of corridors connecting it with a wider wooded environment. This enbles the squirrel to forage further afield in times of shortage without crossing open ground and being exposed to predators. It also allows young squirrels to disperse and interchange to take place with other nearby squirrel populations.

Squirrels in your garden

Jeff Rudge of Bouldnor lives on the edge of the best squirrel territory on the Island. BBC's Nature Detective series featured his attempts to count the number of squirrels visiting his window box to feed last year. The squirrels had become so tame that Jeff could put a blob of paint on each new visitor. After counting twelve in this manner he gave up! He can sit in the garden with food on his lap and bolder squirrels will climb his legs to feed. Lucky Jeff!

Not all cats have a taste for squirrels. In a garden at Brook where squirrels feed for most of the day the owner has two cats. Whilst I was there photographing one afternoon outside on the patio one of these cats jumped onto my lap and sat there as I clicked away at the squirrels who were feeding nearby.

Another garden in Bouldnor is my favourite haunt for photographing squirrels. They arrive in droves with up to 10 squabbling over who feeds on the coconuts and peanuts. Sitting quietly only a few metres away with all this activity to photograph is marvellous. Also seated in the midst of this melee is the owner's cat. Squirrels and cat seem totally oblivious to each other - perhaps the cat doesn't recognise squirrels as 'fair game'.

For garden feeding squirrels, peanuts, hazelnuts and walnuts are very popular as well as being nutritious. Coconuts are another favourite but bread, maize, macaroons, sunflower seeds, apples, raisins and potatoes have all been taken from bird tables, although the food value in some instances is questionable! This is surprisingly true of brazil nuts; the oils they contain cause digestive problems if eaten in quantity. Make sure all food is fresh.

A regular supply of food will attract squirrels to your garden but good aerial routeways can also help. I learnt from one West Wight resident that squirrels stopped visiting his garden when he reduced the height of a thick hedge. They still used his neighbour's garden!

Do be careful about putting food out for squirrels if they have to cross a busy road to reach your garden. They don't seem to have any idea of road safety at all!

It would be possible to provide an artificial drey in your garden but any box-like structure would also be very attractive to birds. A large box with a large hole could even attract owls! Not the best garden companions for your squirrels. I don't know of anyone who has persuaded squirrels to take up residence in an artificial home but if you know differently perhaps you could let me know.

One lady who has fed squirrels, in her front porch, for many years, told me of two strange thefts. One squirrel stole an orange. This is strange squirrel fayre but presumably it was taken to eat. The other incident was even more bizarre. A squirrel took a duster and carried it off into the trees! Was its drey in need of a clean or did the duster make a cosy nest lining? It is thought that squirrels do not readily see colour, except for the yellow/orange range, so perhaps the colour was the attraction.

An unfortunate incident in Ryde meant a trip to the vet for one male squirrel. The squirrel visited a garden daily to feed on peanuts. One day it was noticed that the animal had something around its middle. Several days later it had slipped and tightened around his groin. A trap was taken to the garden and luckily the right squirrel was caught in a short time. The offending material turned out to be a length of fishing line which had tightened round the squirrel's scrotum while he was in full breeding condition - OUCH! He was released in the garden the next day but the scar was visible for a long time.

Photo 22 - Garden Squirrels

Photo 23 - 'Fishing line incident'

Photo 24 - Reversible feet are a necessity for running down trees

Photo 25 - Hedgecutting

DISTRIBUTION

Historic Distribution on the Isle of Wight

It has been said that a squirrel could travel from one end of the Island to the other without touching the ground. This may have been true when squirrels first arrived but its certainly not true today! Many changes have taken place over the centuries and squirrel habitat has been reduced to a shadow of its former glory.

From the Neolithic period onwards woods have been lost and the Island landscape dramatically altered because of the developing needs of agriculture. On the lighter soils in the south of the Island no sizeable woods of ancient origin remain but in the north, where the heavy clays were much harder to work, the percentage of woodland cover is higher.

The development of coppicing dates from the time of the first woodland clearances and the planting of hazel would certainly have benefitted squirrels. During this century though, most coppice has ceased to be actively worked and as the abandoned hazel stools deteriorate the nut crop falls, depriving the Red Squirrel of one of its most prized foods.

The provision of housing for an expanding population, in both towns and villages has destroyed or fragmented squirrel habitat and the development of industry has also taken its toll.

The farming practice of ripping out hedgerows has destroyed or disrupted vital corridors which once linked the now fragmented areas of squirrel habitat. Many of the remaining hedges are trimmed to resemble a 'garden hedge' and although squirrels have been spotted using these 'neat' hedges a tall uncut hedgerow provides a safer passageway and also provides a snack by way of fruits and berries en route.

In 1909 Frank Morey writing in his 'Guide to the Isle of Wight' gives an account of how the Red Squirrel was faring at that time.

> 'The squirrel is to be seen in almost every wood and plantation on the North side of the Island, and is especially plentiful in the woods at Swainston and in Parkhurst Forest. It is less common in the South of the Island. Sometimes a few squirrels will migrate from the woods travelling along the hedges until they reach the trees on the outskirts of the towns. Although the animals are decidedly harmful they are not much persecuted; though old countrymen have told me that formerly squirrel-hunts were organised and if the hunters were successful, the victims were converted into pies.'

By 1934 the situation had changed, probably as a result of disease, as Percy Wadham noted in the Proceedings of the Isle of Wight Natural History and Archaeolgical Society.

'This interesting and delightful animal has, I am sorry to say, become very scarce in the Island. In some other counties on the mainland it is reported that the British Red Squirrel has also become scarce and the fact has been attributed to the introduction of the American Grey Squirrel, but I should favour the view that some disease has overtaken the species and reduced its numbers.'

Thirty years ago squirrels' dreys could be seen in great numbers in Parkhurst Forest, but now one has to hunt a long time to find these nests, and Mr. Fallick, the head game keeper of the well wooded Swainston Estate, informs me that it is seldom he sees a squirrel nowadays.'

Some of the largest tracts of woodland are the conifer plantations at Bouldnor, Parkhurst and Firestone Copse planted after the First World War when the Forestry Commission was formed to stimulate the national production of timber. Brighstone Forest with its large component of beech was planted on downland between the 30s and 50s. These commercial plantations have redressed the balance slightly and provide areas of favourable habitat at least until they are felled.

It is true that there is a greater tree cover now on the Island than at any time in the recorded past (certainly since the late medieval period). The tree cover is, however, in larger blocks which are more isolated from one another and it is the linkage, by way of rough bushy land, hedges, narrow strips of woodland which are much rarer. So, although covering a large acreage, squirrel habitat is not of the same quality as in former times, lacking the corridors and the food supply they provided.

Recent Changes

Although the elm is not a significant food source for squirrels the wholesale loss of trees caused by dutch elm disease probably severed or reduced the number of aerial routeways and led to further losses of hedges.

The 1987 'hurricane' and subsequent violent storms had a major impact on the Island's population of Red Squirrels. All woods were affected but damage was most serious in the commercial conifer plantations and in some areas, especially around Brighstone and the Longstone, the destruction was almost total.

The effects of the storms often come up in conservations about squirrels. 'I always saw them at .....before the storms' is a common response and I'd be rich if I had a pound for every time I've heard that comment. However, by 1992 the population had recovered in most woods, but the overall effect has been a further reduction in numbers because tree cover has been lost and habitat fragmented.

Present distribution on the Isle of Wight

Very little by way of scientific research has been carried out into squirrel numbers and distribution on the Island. Jessica Holm was here from 1983 to 1987. She carried out detailed studies of squirrel ecology and behaviour in particular broadleaved woods but did not study the Island's population as a whole. The late Oliver Frazer MBE collated squirrel sightings on behalf of the Isle of Wight Natural History and Archaeological Society (IOWNHAS) and produced a distribution map covering the period 1960-1991. Some of the information for this map came from a survey carried out by Clive Burland, a teacher at Solent Middle School, with the assistance of 38 Island schools and members of the public. This is one of the few yardsticks available.

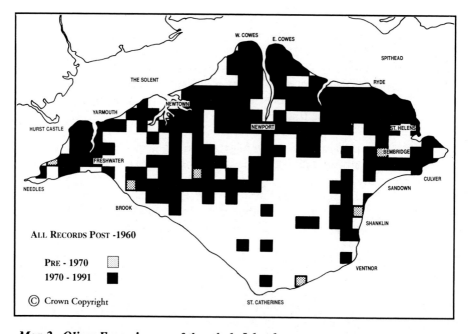

Map 2. Oliver Frazer's map of the whole Island

Oliver Frazer's map showing where Red Squirrels were seen between 1960 and 1991. A 1 km square grid has been used.

Since 1991 I have looked for squirrel evidence in most woods and copses on the Island and from the result of this survey and the numerous reported sightings from members of the public I have been able to put together a reasonably accurate map of current squirrel distribution.

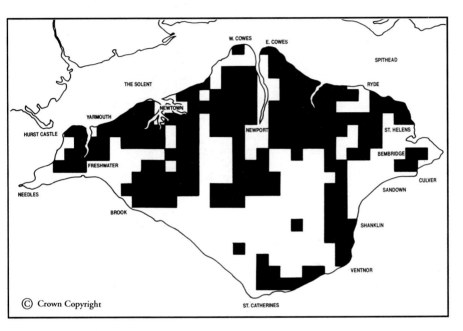

Map 3. Current distribution whole Island

My map showing where squirrels were seen and other 'evidence' was found between 1990 and 1994. The 1 km square grid is used again.

The drawback of presenting information in this way is one of scale and so I have produced another map using a .25 km square grid on a wood by wood basis. Black areas show woods which I have visited and found evidence of squirrels or I have had positive reports from. Shaded squares show woods which I have surveyed and found no squirrel evidence in. If you know otherwise, please let me know!

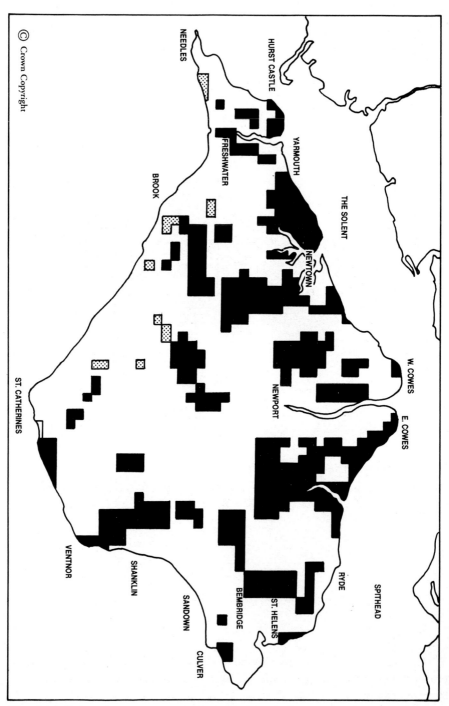

Map using 1/4 km square grid to show woodland on the Island

Red Squirrel status on the Isle of Wight

Large and medium sized broadleaved woods

For the majority of large and medium sized mixed broadleaved woods populations would appear to have remained stable although subject to quite dramatic yearly fluctuations in response to the quality and quantity of the annual food supply. It is worth mentioning here that beech plantations, on their own, do not make good squirrel habitat.

Conifer plantations

The picture is different in the conifer plantations at Bouldnor and Parkhurst. As the trees mature the food source, in the form of cones, is increasing and these places can support higher densities of squirrels. On the other side of the coin the effects of the storms, increased recreational pressures and unsympathetic management can be detrimental to squirrel populations.

The conifer plantations on the downs to the north of Brook and Brighstone have all but disappeared. Already partly felled by the Forestry Commission, they were devastated in the 1987 hurricane and subsequent storms. Large numbers of squirrels have obviously disappeared from the worst affected areas and the remaining tiny population is again vulnerable because the connecting corridors between areas of suitable habitat have been lost and it is possible that the squirrels in the vicinity are only surviving there because they are regulary fed by the local residents.

Small and isolated woods

In smaller woods and areas isolated by the fragmentation of the habitat and loss of corridor links, populations have dwindled and in some cases have disappeared altogether.

The ancient woodland at Borthwood near Alverstone is a beautiful wood enjoyed by many people. With conifers, hazel, and sweet chestnut it should provide a home for a population of squirrels. However this seemingly idyllic setting is not favoured by our Red Squirrels and at present it appears to be home to only one animal. Isolation is the probable cause.

Wooded areas are noticeably absent from South Wight and from the south of Godshill to the southern tip of the Island arable fields dominate the landscape. A few squirrels can be found in the woods at Sainham. These areas are only able to support small populations which become very vulnerable at times of food shortage and their increasing isolation means that recolonisation when numbers are higher is less likely and the long term viability of these populations is questionable.

Urban/semi urban fringe

It is noticeable from the maps that squirrels have disappeared or are seen in much reduced numbers in some urban/semi-urban areas eg Cowes, Ryde, Shanklin, Bembridge and Freshwater and Totland.

Some of this loss is directly attributable to housing/industrial development and the expansion of this activity was quite marked during the 'boom' years of the 1980's. The outskirts of Ryde and Shanklin would fit this pattern with development either directly removing areas of squirrel habitat or disrupting corridors. Shanklin is a good example where continuing development around Sibden Hill is threatening to exclude squirrels from this area of Shanklin.

Freshwater, Totland, and parts of Cowes have been affected by piecemeal development but the situation has been exacerbated by the effects of the 1987 storm when huge numbers of trees were blown down. Many of these were conifers, planted in Victorian times, which provided a vital food supply. Loss of aerial routeways has also been important. The storms would appear to have been a watershed with many people commenting that squirrels were regularly seen in the area before the storms but seldom encountered since. In Freshwater and Totland the squirrel population must now be regarded as vulnerable with much decreased sightings and squirrels confined to small, relatively isolated pockets of woodland, eg. Afton Marsh and Bowbridge Copse.

In Bembridge squirrels have all but disappeared with virtually no recent sightings. The future for squirrels here looks bleak. Loss of trees and grubbing out of hedges has further fragmented an already marginal habitat and with the main road, railway line and river acting as barriers recolonisation becomes increasingly difficult. Bembridge is now effectively isolated and sadly squirrel sightings there may now be a thing of the past.

A comparison of maps 2 and 3 shows an apparent expansion in squirrel sightings in the Undercliff between St. Catherine's Point and Ventnor. It is not clear why this should be but it is possible that this area was under-recorded in the past.

Further research is required to increase our knowledge but as a 'best guess' taking into account the available information the overall state of play on the Island can be summarised as follows:

TABLE 5 Squirrel status on the Isle of Wight

1) Large and medium-sized broad-leaved woods - numbers stable.
2) Small and isolated woods of all types - numbers falling.
3) Large intact conifer plantations - numbers stable but likely to reduce as felling continues as the harvesting stage is reached.
4) Urban/semi urban fringe - numbers declining/critical

Numbers estimate

To get an exact figure for the number of Red Squirrels on the Island would involve intensive trapping under licence from English Nature. This method is costly and time-consuming and there is little likelihood of carrying out this sort of research unless it can be grant aided. A rough estimate can be obtained however by working out the 'carrying capacity' of each wood (ie. estimating how many squirrels live in each piece of woodland) and totalling the figures. Working on this basis I estimate that the Island has around 1000 Red Squirrels in residence. I must emphasise that this is only a rough estimate as numbers fluctuate wildly from year to year and also show marked seasonal variations.

Following her research in the '80s, Jessica Holm estimated the Island population at between 2050 and 4100 squirrels. I think the numbers have definitely reduced since then, probably as a result of a combination of tree loss, following the storms, continuing fragmentation of suitable squirrel habitat and the harvesting of mature conifer plantations.

Status in mainland Britain

Historically the Red Squirrel was widespread over the whole of the British Isles and Ireland arriving after the end of the last Ice Age.

Although periodically suffering losses through disease it was man's impact on the countryside which began to alter the status and distribution of the squirrel. In the 15th century the Red Squirrel disappeared entirely from Irish soil and was not reintroduced until the 19th century. Forest destruction on a dramatic scale to service the needs of agriculture and war was believed to be responsible.

In Wales and Scotland the squirrels decined rapidly during timber shortages of the 15th and 16th centuries and during the 18th century Scottish Reds plummeted almost to the point of extinction although the reasons for this rapid decline are not completely understood.

In England similar deforestation took place but the squirrels did not suffer so badly. The beginning of the 19th century saw tree planting on a large scale, especially of fast growing conifers, and by 1900 the Red Squirrel had reached peak numbers. The story and subsequent decline after this point is intimately linked with the arrival of the Grey Squirrel on British shores.

Arrival of the Greys

SQUIRREL FACT
The Latin name for the Grey Squirrel is Sciurus carolinensis.

The first release of Grey Squirrels is thought to have taken place in 1876 when a Mr Brocklehurst released a pair into the grounds of Henbury Park in Cheshire. Over thirty further introductions took place in the ensuing years but the best known were at Woburn Park in Bedfordshire and it was stock from this location that were released into Regent's Park in London.

From this point on the Greys began a remorseless advance. Between 1900 and 1925 the Reds suffered a dramatic decline all over the British Isles. This may have been part of a natural cycle of disease exacerbated by overcrowding, food shortage, bad weather, habitat destruction and increased pressure from the expanding Greys. Although Greys may have contributed to the problem they were not the cause of it because in areas where they were absent the Red Squirrels were still affected.

Timber requirements for the Second World War and a series of cruel winters between 1939 and 1943 hastened the continuing fall in Red numbers. The Grey squirrel expanded enormously not being so susceptible to the parapoxvirus and evolutionally better suited to exploit the broadleaved woodlands.

Since that time Reds have continually lost ground. No Reds are present in southern Britain except on offshore islands.

SQUIRREL FACT
Situation on Anglesey - The Greys eventually made it across the road bridge thus sealing the fate of the Reds.

Populations can now only be found in the conifer plantations of Norfolk and in some parts of northern England, Wales, Scotland and Ireland.

SQUIRREL FACT
Greys are still colonising Britain moving at the rate of six miles a year. Frontline - Moving south from Glasgow and north from the Pennines into the South Lakes and Cumbria.

All the Red Squirrel populations on mainland Britain appear to be vulnerable and without protective measures are likely to be faced with eventual extinction. The question is, why? What is it about the Grey that makes it an irresistable force as far as the Red is concerned?

Reds vs Greys
Why Reds lose out when Greys appear is a complicated question and as yet no definitive answer has emerged from the extensive research that has been carried out into the subject. It is likely that a whole series of factors are involved:-

TABLE 6 - Why Reds lose out to Greys

1. It was thought initially that Greys were simply the more aggressive species and killed or drove out the Reds from their territories. This is not the case but Red Squirrels may be intimidated by the presence of a larger species and coping with a competitor in terms of territory, food etc may increase stress levels in Reds and make them more susceptible to disease.

2. Greys are not so susceptible to the parapoxvirus.

3. Greys are not so timid. They seem to be more adventurous and are more willing to cross open country.

4. Greys evolved to live in broadleaved woods - Reds evolved in coniferous woods - Greys, therefore, are more likely to survive better at times of food shortage. Eg. Reds cannot remove the toxins in acorns as effectively ᴸs Greys. This causes digestive problems and Reds lose weight rapidly on a predominantly acorn diet.

5. Greys live in larger and denser numbers utilising broadleaf habitat more effectively than the Reds.

6. Greys chase Red females during the mating season which may inhibit or reduce Reds breeding success.

7. Greys eat the hazel nuts before they are ripe. Reds usually wait until they are ripe before eating them but by then of course there may be none left.

8. Reds only put on about 10% of their body weight at the onset of the winter months, Greys increase their bodyweight by at least 20%. Faced with a lean spell and in competition with Greys for food Reds are less likely to survive.

9. Greys will sometimes eat nuts cached by Reds.

10. In overcrowded conditions Reds stop breeding and may even die from stress.

Table 7 Reds and Greys - comparison size and weight

		Red Squirrel	Grey Squirrel
Size			
	Body	220 mm	260 mm
	Tail	180 mm	220 mm
Weight		300 g	550 g

Whatever the causes there is no doubt that once the Greys arrive the Reds disappear, a sorry state of affairs repeated throughout Britain. There is no record of Reds retaking territory lost to Greys. It would seem therefore that the whole of the mainland population is at risk. The only possible exception being extensive tracts of pure conifer plantations where it is believed that the Red Squirrel has a competitive advantage over its transatlantic cousin. If the takeover staged by the Grey is in fact unstoppable then the position of offshore Islands, such as the Isle of Wight and Brownsea Island in Poole Harbour, as sanctuaries, becomes extremely important.

Future threats to the survival of the Red Squirrel on the Isle of Wight

Obviously the major threat to mainland squirrels is the continuing advance of the Greys. The threats to Island squirrels can be summarised as follows:-

1. Arrival of the Grey Squirrel

If the Grey Squirrel ever managed to establish a viable population on the Island Reds would be doomed to extinction. Greys colonising the Island by swimming the Solent is not a realistic possibility. A misguided attempt at a deliberate introduction is a more likely scenario.

The Yarmouth Grey

In fact a Grey Squirrel did arrive on the Island in the early 60's courtesy of the Lymington to Yarmouth ferry. At Yarmouth the disorientated animal leapt from the ferry onto the quay. The threat of a Grey arriving on the Island was well understood and the chase was on! An eye witness recalls seeing the unfortunate creature spreadeagled on the wall of Yarmouth Castle as it tried to make good its escape. It was eventually captured when a man on top of the castle wall drove the terrified creature towards a man in a boat below who was waiting with a long-handled net. It was sent back on the next ferry but its eventual fate is unknown.

Occasional reports of Greys are made but it is thought that these are Red Squirrels with greyish coats.

2. Tunnel or Bridge linking the Island with the Mainland

Proposals for some form of fixed link with the mainland are discussed at regular intervals and at the time of writing interest is being expressed in a tunnel between Ryde and Gosport. Grey Squirrels managed to colonise Anglesey by crossing the road bridge over the Menai Straight so any permanent link with the mainland is bound to increase the risk of Greys arriving with disastrous consequences. Although the Government has given a commitment to protect endangered species I doubt whether this fact will carry much weight in the deliberations about a fixed link.

3. Building development

The impact of building development will continue to erode squirrel habitat particularly in the outskirts of towns and villages where the populations are already vulnerable. The present situation in the Sibden Hill area of Shanklin is a good example. Plans that would have severed vital squirrel corridors have been opposed by the Batts Copse Improvement Group which is trying to make sure that development in this area takes into account both the requirements of local people to live in a congenial environment and the needs of wildlife. As a result of the group's activities the 'upper allotments' area has been spared from development and will become public open space. Hazels and pines are included in the planting scheme which in the future will provide a much needed food supply for the squirrels. It will also enable squirrels to continue to be present almost in the heart of Shanklin and will strengthen this part of the routeway which enables interchange between the populations centered on Hungerberry Wood and the America Wood Complex.

Other developments in the pipeline are not so welcome. The proposal to build on the site of the old railway track which is both a squirrel route and Dormouse territory will obviously be detrimental to both these species.

4. Forestry Commission sell off.

The Forestry Commission is progressively selling off its holdings. As a government agency the Forestry Commission is obliged to take account of the needs of wildlife as it carries out its forestry operations. It is by no means clear how the needs of wildlife will be taken into account when these woods are in private hands.

5. Harvesting of conifers.

Conifers in the plantations are now being harvested. This will lead to an overall reduction in food supply available for Red Squirrels because there will be a considerable gap in time before any trees planted now produce cones.

6. Managing commercial conifer plantations

Spacing of trees is important because if they are planted too close together the lower branches die back and seed production is retarded. Felling operations are also disruptive as squirrels leave areas where they are disturbed by the noise of machinery and falling timber and obviously the prime source of food and shelter is removed. Close attention also needs to be paid to thinning operations as over enthusiastic removal can lead to a dramatic drop in squirrel numbers. When felling takes place corridors should be left so that the remaining areas of plantation are connected by arboreal routeways. If the requirements of the Red Squirrel are properly taken into account the harvesting of timber from commercial plantations needs to be a skilful and carefully managed process.

7. Isolation

Continuing loss of hedgerows and changes in uses of farmland may result in some squirrel populations becoming increasingly isolated. Eg. Bembridge. Isolated colonies are much more likely to die out at times of food shortage and because the habitat is becoming increasingly fragmented then recolonisation is far less likely than in the past.

8. Reduced genetic viability

This is a well known problem that affects small, isolated populations but I would suspect these squirrels are much more at risk from food shortages than the effects of having a limited gene-pool.

9. Disease

In the past disease has wrought havoc amongst the Red Squirrel population and the spread of any disease would be extremely worrying considering the current level of squirrel numbers.

10. Recreational pressures

A possible, little studied, threat to our Red Squirrels is the increasing use of their habitat for human recreation. Using woods for our pleasure will help to secure their future, but what impact war games, paintball, motorcycle scrambling and orienteering has on the squirrels is unknown - they probably think we are a very peculiar species. It seems, from my own and other people's observations, that squirrels avoid the busiest routes used by dog walkers.

CONSERVATION

The Government has made several commitments on different levels, regarding biodiversity and wildlife, which directly affect the position of the Red Squirrel.

SQUIRREL FACT
Biodiversity can be defined broadly as ' the number and range of plant and animal species'.

Endangered species

The Red Squirrel receives legal protection as an endangered species under the 1981 Wildlife and Countryside Act. It states that:-

'..It is illegal to damage, destroy or obstruct access to any structural place which animals on schedule 5 use for shelter or protection, or to disturb such an animal whilst it is occupying a structural place which it uses for that purpose..'

So squirrels should not be disturbed, caught or killed and to do so could lead to prosecution and a court appearance. Anyone who studies or has to catch them for any reason needs to have a licence issued by English Nature.

SQUIRREL FACT
Grey Squirrels receive no legal protection - in fact they are classed as 'vermin' and can therefore be caught and killed.

The 'Berne' Convention

This convention covers the conservation of European wildlife and natural habitats. Signatories to the convention undertake to conserve wild plants, birds and other animals especially those that are endangered.

EC Habitat Directive

The aim of this directive is to conserve biodiversity.

'Member states are required to take measures to maintain or restore natural habitats and wild species at a favourable conservation status in the Community, giving effect to both site and species protection objectives'.'

Earth Summit at Rio

This was the conference of global powers that took place in Rio de Janeiro in 1992 to consider the environmental plight of the earth. As a result of this conference the Government signed the Biodiversity agreement. Since then a 'Strategy for Sustainable Development' has been produced which commits the Government *'to conserve and enhance biological diversity within the UK.'*

SQUIRREL FACT
In broad terms, sustainable development means 'meeting the needs of the present without compromising the needs of future generations.'

Some of these commitments the Government has signed up to are very far-reaching and integrating the policy on biodiversity with other government policies implies much greater consideration of the needs of endangered species. As yet there is little evidence of these fine words actually resulting in better protection and a more secure future but several initiatives are underway to try to conserve the Red Squirrel.

Work being done

NPI Red Alert NE & NW
This is a programme set up in Northumberland to monitor Reds in a Grey-free zone. Grey are invading south from Scotland and north from Durham and positive management of the forest is being considered to help the Reds survive.

English Nature's Species Recovery Programme
This covers other endangered species of wildlife including the Natterjack Toad and the Dormouse but has earmarked £46,000 for Red Squirrels. Studies, jointly funded by the Forestry Commission are being carried out at Thetford Forest in East Anglia. It is fronted by Dr John Gurnell a senior lecturer in animal behaviour and ecology at Queen Mary and West field College, London and the main thrust of the work will be to monitor the Red Squirrel population at Thetford and experiment with supplementary feeding, habitat management and Grey Squirrel control.

Other Red Squirrel Conservation Initiatives
Projects are also under way in Clocaenog Forest, Wales, Cannock forest and on the island of Jersey.

Reintroduction and captive breeding

Mainland Britain

This will of course involve either moving existing Grey Squirrels or creating Grey-free buffer zones. The squirrels for reintroductions will be translocated from existing, high density populations or will come from captive breeding programmes. As these schemes, which are in their infancy, depend on implementing permanent measures to keep Greys out, they require continuous funding and their long-term success cannot yet be accurately predicted.

Isle of Wight

The situation is different on the Island. If a wood does not have squirrels the reason is related to the quality of the habitat and not to the lack of squirrels. A reintroduction programme would not address this problem at all and would simply condemn the introduced squirrels to death. The answer here is first to sustain and improve the existing habitat and then to reverse the processes which have fragmented the habitat in the past.

It has been suggested that the Island should have a Red Squirrel sanctuary. This is an excellent idea if a suitable location and funds can be found. A more radical suggestion would be for the Government to declare all of the Isle of Wight as a Red Squirrel sanctuary as part its commitment to protecting the biodiversity of the British Isles.

National Strategy for saving the Red Squirrel

A strategy for saving the Red Squirrel nationwide is being discussed at present and an England Squirrel Committee has been formed to consider priorities. The national strategy will include the Island, although as circumstances on the Island differ greatly from anywhere else in the country a separate strategy will be needed to fit our unique situation. This will require the involvement and cooperation of the Council.

Importance of Island Squirrels in a national context.

The Isle of Wight, apart from its special status of isolation from Grey Squirrels, also has another advantage when it comes to maintaining our Red Squirrel population - there is no opposition from deer. Although almost as endearing as our Red Squirrels, deer are also very destructive. As browsers they destroy the brambles which bear the berries eaten by squirrels and more importantly they nibble at the hazel coppice and retard the growth of the Red Squirrels' most nutritious food source.

The absence of Greys also means that our Island Reds can be studied in a natural environment, free from the effects of competition.

Conservation of Island Squirrels

Consists of the following measures:-

1. Keeping Greys out.

2. Sympathetic management of both broadleaved and conifer woods.

3. Reinstating links in areas where habitat has become fragmented.

4. Ongoing monitoring programme to provide up to date information on the well-being of the squirrel population.

5. Tree planting programme.

6. Needs of endangered species should be taken into account in the planning process. eg. when considering planning application and when considering larger scale reviews, eg 10 year plan, review of A.O.N.B. areas with a commitment to positive measures to improve the situation for squirrels.

What you can do to help

1. Look out for and report tree felling operations which will affect the squirrels in your area.

2. Support organisations interested in Squirrels (sse Appendix 2).

3. Scan the *County Press* for planning applications which will disrupt squirrel habitat or corridors.

4. Report squirrel sightings to Wight Wildlife. This is very helpful for research.

5. If you have squirrels in your garden feeding them at times of natural food shortage can help them survive.

The Future

With the public's increasing awareness of the value of the natural environment and signs that the Government is beginning to take the whole issue of endangered species more seriously, there is hope for the future of the Red Squirrel on the Isle of wight.

Enlightened ideas on management and the growing number of conservation groups will ensure that some of our neglected woodland will receive expert attention and provide a future 'up market' home for our precious squirrels. After all, in the not too distant future, off-shore islands may have the only Red Squirrels left in Britain. It is up to us to fight for the preservation and enhancement of our remaining Island woods to provide a habitat for Red Squirrels and other wildlife as well as for our own recreational pleasure.

There are still many threats but if these can be tackled and cooperation from the Council, landowners and forestry Commission is forthcoming, then the Red Squirrel stands a chance of retaining its precarious hold on at least one small corner of England.

APPENDIX 1.

Where to find squirrels on the Island

The Forestry owned woods, which are very popular with the public and easily accessible, offer reasonable opportunities to see a squirrel. Your chances increase if you are patient enough to sit quietly where squirrel feeding signs are in evidence.

Parkhurst has a good number of squirrels in the Corsican Pine stands - look for the stripped cones here. Similarly at Bouldnor, which is particularly good in the areas which have not been thinned, used cones can be picked up by the handful in a good year and a squirrel flitting amongst the branches should be easily detected.

The Forestry owned Firestone Copse in East Wight is enjoyed by many people and their dogs. Tree species on parts of the main walk are not particularly favoured by squirrels, but again if you look for the Corsican Pine stands, you will know that you are in squirrel territory. Sightings of squirrels are also quite common in the broadleaf area of Firestone Copse. This is where the hazel coppice is found.

Ninham, Apsecastle and America Wood are also popular with walkers and squirrels. I had an encounter with a very angry squirrel here. It seemed to think that all the sweet chestnuts - it was a bumper crop that year - belonged to the Red Squirrels and took great exception to my picking them up as well. This animal was so cross it stayed on the ground only a few metres away - very unusual! - swearing at me and swishing its tail. I even talked to it and told it not to be so greedy, it couldn't possibly eat all those nuts - and it still didn't move!

Walters Copse and Town Copse in Newtown are relatively quiet, small copses so sightings here are more common. This summer I had two interesting encounters with squirrels in Town Copse. I was quietly walking along the path when I heard the angry 'chukking' noise of a red squirrel in the branches of an oak tree. I looked at the squirrel and smiled and thought how pretty it was. The squirrel looked at me and swore, and swished its tail in annoyance, probably thinking 'what are you doing in my territory?'. It then vented its anger on the oak tree by biting the end leaves off a twig and throwing them at me! The second squirrel I saw here a few days later was travelling at head height in the hazel branches carrying dried grass in its mouth - at least it couldn't swear at me with its mouth full!

Tourist Attractions visited by squirrels
Osborne House
Barton Manor
Carisbrooke
Shanklin Chine, Rylstone Gardens, Tower Gardens
St.Lawrence undercliff
Luccombe Chine and Landslip
Fort Victoria
Thorness Holiday Centre
Havenstreet Station

APPENDIX 2

Organisations supporting squirrels

English Nature

Forestry Commission

Mammal Society

National Trust

NPI

People's Trust. for Endangered Species

Royal Society for Nature Conservation

Wildlife Trusts

Wight Wildlife
This is a partnership between the Isle of Wight Natural history and Achaeological Society and the Hampshire & Isle of Wight Wildlife Trust. Both organisations are concerned about the conservation of Red Squirrels and the partnership seeks to promote their conservation through protection and sympathetic management.

APPENDIX 3

Reporting squirrel sightings

Sightings should be reported to Helen Butler c/o

Wight Wildlife
The Gatehouse
Forest Road
Newport
Tel : 522949

You can use the sighting report form provided in Appendix 4. Or better still take a photocopy and pin it up somewhere you can see it and just jot down your sightings and send them off to me every once in a while.

Reporting dead squirrels

If you find a dead squirrel in good condition the body would be useful so that it can be sent off for scientific analysis which can yield all sorts of useful information eg about the health of the squirrel before it died, cause of death, presence of pollutants etc. The body can be kept fresh, in a polythene bag, in the freezer compartment of a refrigerator. I am interested in receiving information on all squirrel deaths (address as above.)

What to do if you find an injured squirrel

The vet, Mr. I. L. Stretch BSc, MRCVS, of 15 Chapel Street, Newport (Tel 520543) has offered to treat all injured squirrels free of charge. He can also be contacted at the following addresses:
2 Foreland Road, Bembridge and 40 High Street, Wootton (Tel: 883955)

This page has been included so as to allow you to record any squirrel sightings or behaviour.

RED SQUIRREL SIGHTING SHEET

Date	Place seen & map grid reference	Remarks

REPORTER: Name: _____

Address: _____

_____

Tel. No: _____

Thank you for your help in Red Squirrel research.